GW00994568

THE WALL THAT DID NOT FALL

THE STORY OF RAHAB'S FAITH

By Marilyn Lashbrook

Illustrated by Stephanie McFetridge Britt

ME TOO!
B O O K S

Treasure!

829 S. Shields · Fort Collins, CO 80521
1-800-284-0158

"The Wall That Did Not Fall" tells
the exciting story of the battle of
Jericho from an insider's viewpoint.
Your little one will see how God
helps us to believe in Him and
protects those who trust Him.
Encourage your child to participate
in the story by making sounds —
knocking, shouting and counting
numbers. Also, after the story has
been read several times, wait for your
child to answer the question, "Why
did they do that?"

The story of Rahab's faith
delightfully illustrates God's saving
power in response to faith. Use it to
talk to your little one about believing
God for salvation.

Library of Congress Catalog Card Number: 87-63420
ISBN 0-86606-433-8

Copyright © 1988 by Roper Press, Inc. All rights reserved.
Printed in the U.S.A.

Art direction and design by
   Chris Schechner Graphic Design

THE WALL THAT DID NOT FALL

THE STORY OF RAHAB'S FAITH

By Marilyn Lashbrook

Illustrated by Stephanie McFetridge Britt

Taken from Joshua 2 and 6

ME TOO!
B O O K S

Rahab looked out her window
to see if Joshua's army was coming.
Knock! Knock! Knock!
Who could be at her door?

Two spies from Joshua's army rushed in.

They had some important
questions to ask.

"Everyone in our city
is afraid of your people,"
Rahab told them.
"The king's soldiers
will be looking for you."

"Hurry!" she whispered. "Follow me."
And the men scrambled
up the stairs after her.

She hid them on the roof under the flax.
It tickled their *noses*
and scratched their *toes*.
But they were quiet and still.

The soldiers came.
The soldiers looked.
The soldiers went.
But they did not find the spies.

So Rahab went back to the roof.
"I know your God
is the God of heaven,"
she said, "and He has
given you this city.

"Promise to help my family
when your army comes
to take Jericho."

"We promise!" said the spies.

Then Rahab dropped
a rope from the window
and the spies climbed out.

"Tie this red cord here," they said,
"and everyone in your house
will be safe."

Rahab believed the spies
and did just what they said.

One day the spies came back,
but they were not alone.

They came with Joshua and his army.
The king and his soldiers
were ready to fight.

But Joshua's army did not fight!
They did not say a word.
They just marched around the city,
and then they marched away.

Why did they do that?

Because God told them to!

The next day the army marched
around the city again.
And once again they left.

Why did they do that?

Because God told them to!

Three, four, five, six days
they marched around the city and left.
But the seventh day was different!

They marched around
1 2 3 4 5 6 7 times.
Why? *Because God told them to!*

Then, just like God said,
the people shouted
as loud as they could. *"Hooray!"*

And the walls of Jericho
began to crumble.

Great stones began to tumble.
What a noisy rumble
as the walls fell down!

But God kept one part
of the wall from falling —
the part with the red cord
tied in the window.

Knock! Knock! Knock!
Rahab knew who it was this time.

She hurried to open the door.
The spies helped her
and her family out to safety.

The sky lit up as the city of Jericho
went up in flames. But Rahab was saved.

She believed in God.
And He kept her safe.

ME TOO!
B O O K S

For Ages 2-5

SOMEONE TO LOVE
THE STORY OF CREATION

TWO BY TWO
THE STORY OF NOAH'S FAITH

"I DON'T WANT TO"
THE STORY OF JONAH

"I MAY BE LITTLE"
THE STORY OF DAVID'S GROWTH

"I'LL PRAY ANYWAY"
THE STORY OF DANIEL

WHO NEEDS A BOAT?
THE STORY OF MOSES

"GET LOST LITTLE BROTHER"
THE STORY OF JOSEPH

THE WALL THAT DID NOT FALL
THE STORY OF RAHAB'S FAITH

NO TREE FOR CHRISTMAS
THE STORY OF JESUS' BIRTH

"NOW I SEE"
THE STORY OF THE MAN BORN BLIND

DON'T ROCK THE BOAT!
THE STORY OF THE MIRACULOUS CATC

OUT ON A LIMB
THE STORY OF ZACCHAEUS

SOWING AND GROWING
THE PARABLE OF THE SOWER AND THE SOI

DON'T STOP . . . FILL EVERY PO
THE STORY OF THE WIDOW'S OIL

GOOD, BETTER, BEST
THE STORY OF MARY AND MARTHA

GOD'S HAPPY HELPERS
THE STORY OF TABITHA AND FRIENDS

ME TOO!
R E A D E R S

For Ages 5-8

IT'S NOT MY FAULT
MAN'S BIG MISTAKE

GOD, PLEASE SEND FIRE!
ELIJAH AND THE PROPHETS OF BAAL

TOO BAD, AHAB!
NABOTH'S VINEYARD

THE WEAK STRONGMAN
SAMSON

NOTHING TO FEAR
JESUS WALKS ON WATER

THE BEST DAY EVER
THE STORY OF JESUS

THE GREAT SHAKE-UP
MIRACLES IN PHILIPPI

TWO LADS AND A DAD
THE PRODIGAL SON

Available at your local bookstore or from

Treasure Publishing

MSC 1000 829 S Shields · Fort Collins, CO 80521
1-800-284-0158